The Golden Carpet

A story from Armenia

Retold by Mairi Mackinnon
Illustrated by Alida Massari

Reading consultant: Alison Kelly
University of Roehampton

There was once a handsome
prince named Aram. He
loved to go out hunting
with his friends.

One summer day, they
came to a village in the hills.

Prince Aram saw a beautiful girl fetching some water from the well.

The prince and his friends were thirsty. "Give us a drink of water!" they cried.

The girl poured water on a cloth. "Please, wipe your faces first," she said.

Then she poured some
more water into a cup
for them.

"Why did you do that?"
the prince asked.

"If you drink too quickly, it can make you sick," the girl explained.

You needed to cool down.

She smiled and went away.
Prince Aram was amazed.
"Who is she?" he wondered.

His friends asked the villagers. "That's Ani, the shepherd's daughter," they said proudly.

She taught everyone in our village to read.

Clever Ani.

"I am going to marry her,"
Aram decided.

His friends were shocked.
"You can't make a shepherd
girl into a princess!"

But that evening, the prince went to the shepherd's house. It was full of fine carpets and lace.

My daughter Ani made everything here.

"I want to marry your daughter!" Aram burst out. "Well then, you should ask her yourself," said the shepherd.

Ani laughed. "I don't know anything about you. What do you do?"

"I'm a prince," Aram said with pride.

"You can't just be a prince," said Ani. "Can't you do anything else?"

I will only marry a man who knows how to do a real job.

"Ani is right. I really should learn a skill," the prince thought.

When he returned to his palace, Aram called for the best craftsmen in the city. "What can you teach me?" he asked.

One old man stepped forward. "Your Majesty, I can show you how to weave carpets threaded with gold."

That would be a fine skill for a prince.

The prince worked hard,
and learned all he could.

   A year later, he went back
to Ani's village with a
beautiful carpet.

It had a pattern of flowers
and birds and golden crowns
around Ani's own name.

Soon after, Ani married
Prince Aram. In time, they
became King and Queen.

They ruled wisely and
well, and all their people
loved them.

The King and his friends still liked to go hunting. One day, they rode into the hills, many miles from the palace.

When it started getting
dark, they made a fire and
set up camp for the night.

Suddenly, thick black smoke rolled around them. Invisible enemies attacked from all sides.

Invisible hands tied them together and forced them to march through the night.

As the dawn broke, they
reached high cliffs and
trudged into a cave.

Once they were inside,
the cave mouth closed
behind them.

Torches flickered, and at last they saw who had captured them – a cruel sorcerer.

"You are my slaves!"
thundered the sorcerer.
"Work for me, and I might
just spare your lives."

He led them into a vast cavern. In the dim light, they saw men and women hunched over looms and workbenches.

You'll die unless you do as he says.

Aram was horrified, but he was determined to save his friends. "Sir, we are weavers," he said.

We can make the finest carpet you have ever seen.

"We'll need fine wool
and gold thread, and the
biggest loom you have."

The sorcerer's slaves worked
day and night. Their master
took everything they made,
and sold it in the city.

Aram secretly taught his
friends all the skills he knew.
Gradually, a beautiful carpet
took shape.

And into the border, the
King wove a secret message...

When the sorcerer saw the finished carpet, he was impressed.

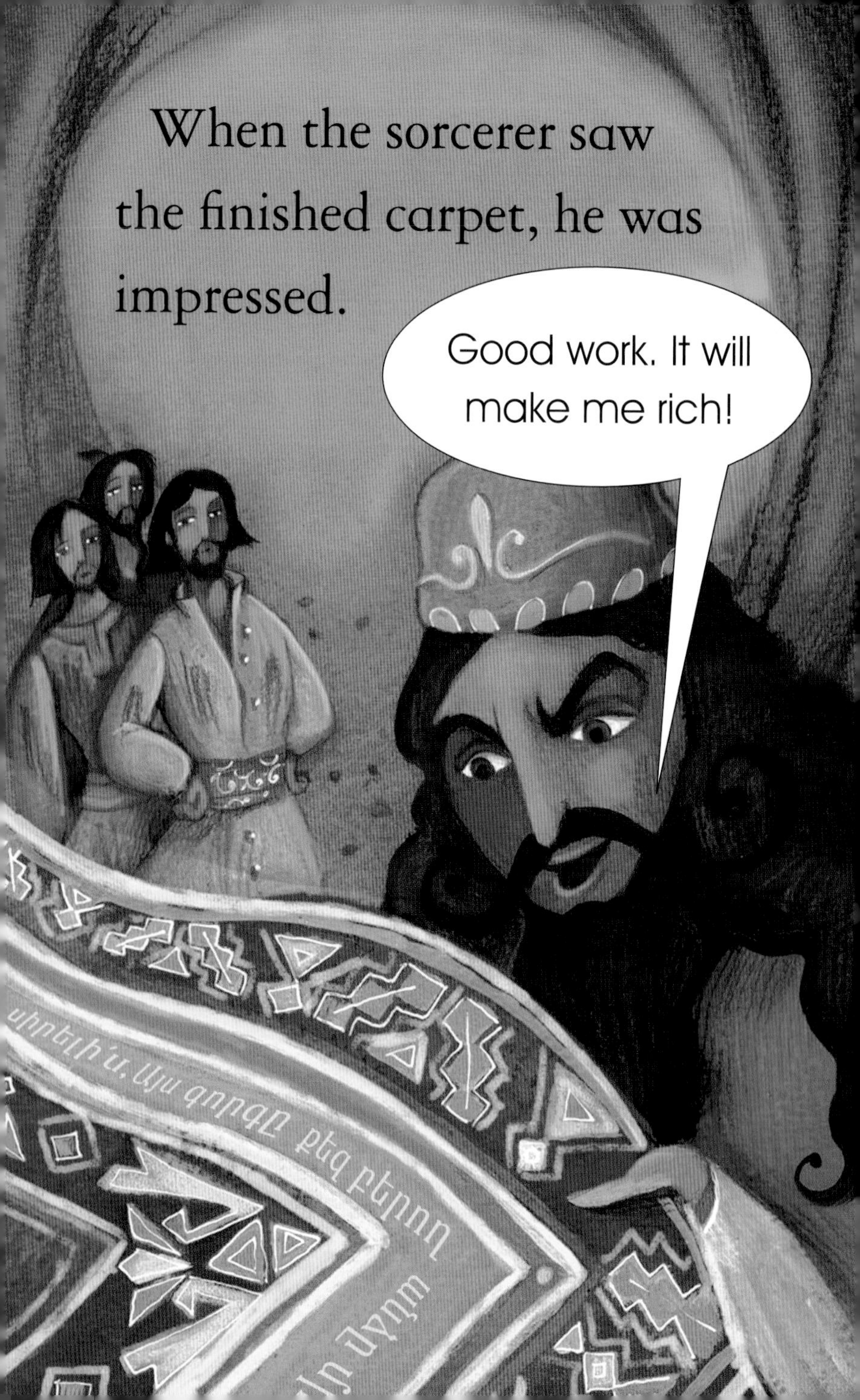

"You should show it to the
Queen," Aram said. "She will
give you the best price for it."

All this time, Queen Ani
had been desperately worried.

She sent out one search
party after another, but there
was no news. Still, she was
sure that the King was alive.

One day, she heard that a
strange old man wanted to
show her a fine carpet. Ani
felt a surge of hope.

She recognized the King's work right away. Then she spotted the secret message:

MY DARLING,

THE MAN WHO BROUGHT YOU THIS CARPET IS AN EVIL SORCERER. WE ARE HIS PRISONERS IN THESE MOUNTAINS. HELP US!

"Please, lend me your stick," the Queen said to the old man. "I need to spread the carpet out a little." She took his magic staff.

Then she cried, "Guards, seize him!" The sorcerer screeched and writhed, but without his staff he was helpless.

Queen Ani herself rode to the mountains to rescue the King. When she reached the cliff, she struck it hard with the sorcerer's staff.

The staff snapped and the cave opened. The slaves saw bright daylight and cheered. Aram rushed into Ani's arms.

I knew you would save us.

The Queen brought the slaves back to the palace, and sent for their families. Soon they were all strong and well.

So were Aram and his friends, although they weren't so keen on hunting any more.

King Aram and Queen Ani
ruled for many more years.
Their palace became more
and more splendid.

It was filled with beautiful
things, made by the King
and Queen...

...their children...

...and all their friends.

The Golden Carpet is a folk tale from Armenia, in Central Asia. It is also known as *The Golden Bracelet*, from the idea that a skill is like a golden bracelet, a treasure you keep for your whole life.

With thanks to the Armenian Institute in London
Designed by Caroline Spatz
Series designer: Russell Punter
Series editor: Lesley Sims

First published in 2013 by Usborne Publishing Ltd., Usborne House, 83-85 Saffron Hill, London EC1N 8RT, England. www.usborne.com
Copyright © 2013 Usborne Publishing Ltd.